Edition Schott

Edition Konrad Ragossnig

Isaac Albéniz
1860 – 1909

Asturias

Leyenda

für Gitarre
for Guitar
pour Guitare

aus / from / de: „Suite española"
opus 47/5

Bearbeitet von / Arranged by / Arrangée par
Konrad Ragossnig

GA 445
ISMN 979-0-001-09694-2

www.schott-music.com

Mainz · London · Berlin · Madrid · New York · Paris · Prague · Tokyo · Toronto

»Asturias« wurde von Konrad Ragossnig auf Schallplatte bei der Firma Claves (Schweiz), in der Bundesrepublik Deutschland vertreten durch „Disco-Center", Kassel, aufgenommen („Spanische Gitarremusik")

ASTURIAS

(Leyenda)

No. 5 aus „Suite española", opus 47*)

Eingerichtet für Gitarre von / Arranged for guitar by
Konrad Ragossnig

Isaac Albéniz
1860—1909

*) Original für Klavier

*) Flageolett 8va alta ad libitum

poco rit.
a tempo
poco rit.
a tempo
decresc.
D.C.al Φ poi Coda
Coda
sul ponticello
loco
pizz.
8va

*)Vgl. Seite 5